VOLUME

PLANET KASPER

COMIX & TRAGIX
PETER SCHUMANN

Fomite
Burlington, VT

ISBN-13: 978-1-937677-19-0
Library of Congress Control Number:

Fomite
58 Peru Street
Burlington, VT 05401
www.fomitepress.com

KASPER 15   1
   SPRING
KASPER 16   15
   THE RAVENS
KASPER 17   29
   SNOW
KASPER 18   43
   GOD
KASPER 19   57
   AGAIN
KASPER 20   71
   THE ETHICAL CLEANING
      CORPORATION
KASPER 21   85
   FOREIGN AFFAIRS
KASPER 22   99
   SCHNAPS
KASPER 23   113
   KASPER'S HORSES
KASPER 24   127
   KASPER VISITS
     THE CHAIRS
KASPER 25   141
   KASPER'S SCISSORS NINETOLOGY

KASPER 26   155
    THIS IS KASPER'S DIVINA SHOPPING COMEDIA
    OR: HOW TO REDESIGN THE WORLD TO ACHIEVE
    THE POLITICALLY CORRECT POST-MODERN PARADISE
        PART 1: PARADISE
        PART 2: INFERNO

KASPER 27   169
GENERAL KASPER'S HEARTFELT DISPATCHES
            TO HIS SOLDIERS

KASPER 28   183
    A JOB
    KASPER 29   197
    DUCK SOUP

Introduction

The British call him Punch, the Italians, Pulchinello, the Russians, Petruchka, the Native Americans, Coyote. These are the figures we may know. But every culture that worships authority will breed a Punch-like, anti-authoritan resister. Yin and yang -- it has to happen. The Germans call him Kasper.

Truth-telling and serious pranking are dangerous professions when going up against power. Bradley Manning sits naked in solitary; Julian Assange is pursued by Interpol, Obama's Department of Justice, and Amazon.com. But -- in contrast to merely human faces -- masks and theater can often slip through the bars.

Consider our American Kaspers: Charlie Chaplin, Woody Guthrie, Abby Hoffman, the Yes Men -- theater people all, utilizing various forms to seed critique. Their profiles and tactics have evolved along with those of their enemies.

Who are the bad guys that call forth the Kaspers? Over the last half century, with his Bread & Puppet Theater, Peter Schumann has been tireless in naming them, excoriating them with Kasperdom.

* * * * * * * * * * *

An early, iconic Schumann naming of the perps occurs at the end of Bread & Puppet's mid-60s Christmas Story:

After the news spreads of Jesus's birth, King Herod picks up the phone:

"Hello, Third Army? Go straight to Bethlehem and kill all the children."

In the next scene a large soldier marches in, in full battle array, and knocks on the door of a tiny puppet house. "Good evening, Ma'am. Do you happen to have any children in the house?"
"Oh, yes, of course," the little hand-puppet says. "Hansie and Mariechen."
"Can you bring them out, please?"
"Oh certainly, Sergeant. But...why?
"We want to kill them."
"Oh."

The mother then tells the sergeant an amazing story that he'll "never believe, but..." about how the children were just taking a bath and then -- by accident -- they were washed down the drain. The sergeant, stupefied, weeps.

"Oh, lady, that's really terrible. Allow me to extend the condolences of the entire Third Army."

He marches off to the next house where he finds that the six children happened to have just marched off six weeks ago and haven't come back yet.

"Men, King Herod isn't going to be too pleased about this."

The next house turns out to be the Bethlehem Nursery, "And we have 55 sweet, little darlings fast asleep in their sweet little beddy-byes," says the Nurse out her window, "AND YOU GORILLAS ARE WAKING THEM UP WITH YOUR SCREAMING. You better go play soldier somewhere else, or I'll call the authorities."

"Lady," says the sergeant, "we are the authorities."

There's the key. Who is the enemy that must call forth the Kaspers? The men and ideas that people must turn to for help -- the authorities themselves.

For a while at Bread & Puppet, they were portrayed as "the Butchers" -- figures in black suits and little black hats. White faces with no eyes. They did bad things like kill white horses, and had to be overcome.

They had what Schumann called rotten ideas, and it is later with the Rotten Idea Theater Company that their plans are often and comically presented. And who presents them? Kaspers! Four-foot grotesque masks on five to six foot bodies, tiny legs under them scurrying around, great foam-rubber slapstick clubs, swinging, reducing all to chaos.

A brilliant satirical, even obvious, strategy -- to present social/political norms with the most abnormal faces. If the mask fits, wear it.

So Kasper wakes again in contemporary America, needed, perhaps, as never before. His current playground is Glover, Vermont, a town of a thousand in the Northeast Kingdom of Vermont. His current birth- and nursing-place is in the heartmindhands of Peter Schumann.

* * * * * * * * * * * * * * * *

In this volume you have a graphic Kasperdom, a comic book presenting a comic but serious character in comic but dead-serious circumstances. Who are the bad guys in Planet Kasper? The intelligent smooth machinists of capitalism and its "responsible" lifestyle. That is, the powerful of Western "Civilization".

Gandhi, when asked what he thought of Western Civilization, famously replied, "I think it would be a good idea."

Schumann's critique is far more radical, imbued with a modern understanding of the results of Faustian striving. In Planet Kasper, he extols some very non-rotten ideas as alternatives: embracing the unbusiness, great beauty and mysterious nonsense of the naked universe. A life dedicated to non-acceptance of garbage society values.

What does Peter Schumann think of western civilization? Read this book.

* *

Western civilization has small purchase on life at Glover. Yes, though they grow much of their own, the puppeteers must buy some food in stores. They must put gas in their touring vehicles. Beyond that, "modern" life is minimal -- the Schumanns have no computer, and if they did, they couldn't really do much with no broadband available. Cell phones don't work. During the summer a hundred people live in tents and shit in outhouses. And though there are no reviews, and no advertising, thousands come to see and applaud them. The entrance fee is zero.

But the cost to spectators is high. While most are already disposed to Peter Schumann's Bread & Puppet critique, they, unlike the puppeteers, must drive back home to cognitive dissonance and highlighted, admitted contradictions.

You can read your copy of Planet Kasper for chuckles. You can read it for a further glimpse into the head of that guy on the back cover blowing two horns. Or you can take it seriously -- as seriously as your life will permit. Or you can change your life.

It's that kind of a book.

Marc Estrin
Burlington, Vermont, 2011
as the power plants of western civilization burn and spew.

BREAD & PUPPET

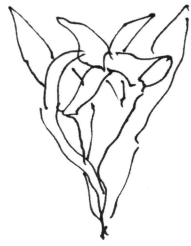

KASPER 15

3

7

9

11

BREAD&PUPPET
PRESS 2006

BREAD & PUPPET

KASPER 16

FIRST KASPER CONTEMPLATES THE GRANDPAS
THE KIND THAT LIVE IN THE DITCHES BY THE
SIDE OF THE SUPERIOR HIGHWAYS, TUGGED
AWAY SNUGLY WITH THEIR GRADMAS,
INDISCRIMINATELY O.K. AMID SWAMP-
GRASSES. THE TRUCKS & OTHER SUPERIOR
FORMS OF LIFE RATTLE BY THEM, NEVER MIND.
COZILY THEY SIT THERE IN THEIR
FAVORITE DITCH, OH HOW LOVELY
IS THE EVENING UP THERE
IN THE NORTH WHERE PEOPLE GROW
COLD EGGS & WHEN THE TIME IS RIPE, THEY PAINT
THEM FOR THEIR GRANDCHILDREN.
THIS PARTICULAR ONE IS CALLED RUMPEL-
BRAIN BECAUSE OF A CERTAIN IMBALANCE
IN HIS ORIENTATION DEPARTMENT & THE GRANDMA
IS CALLED MS. HUMPELBEIN ON ACCOUNT OF HER
LIMPING. THEY PULL BLANKETS OVER THEIR HEADS
WHEN THINGS GET TOO OUTRAGEOUS OR WHEN THE
SUPERIOR HIGHWAY TOSSES ITS ROADKILL TOO CLOSE
TO THEIR HEARTS. SILLY, ISN'T IT TO LIVE IN A DITCH
WHEREAS THE AVAILABLE GRAND STYLE OF LIFE IS THE
OPPOSITE OF A DITCH.   OH YES, FROM
THE STANDPOINT   OF THE ELEGANT
BEINGS WHO WE CALL MODERN HUMANITY, GENERALLY
HARD WORKING, HARD VACATIONING MODERNISTS, THERE
ISN'T MUCH TO IT, TO THIS LIFE IN THE DITCH

①

BECAUSE ALL THE BEAUTY OF LIFE IS FOUND AT
THE END OF THE SUPERIOR HIGHWAY THE
GLAMOROUS XMASPARTY SKYLINE FOLLOWED BY A
WONDERFUL MOUNTAINOUS TERRAIN MADE OF THE
BEST MATERIALS WHICH MAYBE A LITTLE HARD ON
THE FEET
(& IS DEFINITELY
NOT MEANT FOR
THE FEET) BUT FOR THE HUMAN CENTER WHERE THE
PENETRATION MACHINERY IS LOCATED & DEMANDS
PENETRATION OF ANY KIND, ESPECIALLY THE
LUXURY CONCRETENESS WHICH LIES AT THE END OF
THE SUPERIOR HIGHWAY. OH! SAYS MR. RUMPELBRAIN
OH! SAYS MS. HUMPELBEIN, LET'S COOK OUR ROADKILL-
SPECIAL & CHASE THE CHICKENS FROM THE COOP, THEY
NEED SUNLIGHT. OH YOU SUNLIGHT!
AND THEN KASPER LISTENS TO THE
BAKER WHOSE BREAD IS NOT
CONNECTED TO THE STORE. THE
STORE IS TOO SAD SAYS THE BAKER
BUT BEMOANING THE STORE DOESN'T HELP, BETTER
TO AVOID IT LIKE THE DEVASTATED SITUATIONS
WHICH TRAIL REFUGEES & THEIR CHILDREN BEHIND
THE HARVESTERS & THEY GLEAN THE RYE & THE
WHEAT & THE PRICKLY STUBBLES BLOODY THE KIDS'
ANKLES BUT NEVERTHELESS SAY THANK YOU & THE
KIDS ANSWER YOU'RE WELCOME.

(2)

18

NEXT THE RISING RAUCOUS BAND PLAYS FOOT MUSIC
WHICH PRODUCES DANCE & DANCE SUBJECTED TO
FIERCE MUSIC THRESHES THE GRAIN

& EXCITES HUMAN LAZINESS WHICH SITS AROUND
& WAITS FOR INSTRUCTIONS BUT INSTRUCTIONS HAVE
LONG RUN OUT OF INSTRUCTIVENESS ONLY THE DANCE
HAPPILY THRESHES THE GRAIN & THE REFUGEES
CALL THIS DANCING PURPOSE DANCING & THEY DON'T
HAVE TO UNSUFFOCATE THEMSELVES FROM THE
OVERWROUGHT BECAUSE THEY ARE NORMAL
REFUGEES ALREADY & PROBABLY EVERYBODY
WILL EVENTUALLY BECOME REFUGEE. BETTER TO
STUDY REFUGEEDOM WHICH IS RELATED TO THE
ORIGINAL HUMAN CULTURE & THEREFORE ALMOST
INDISTRUCTABLE

(ONLY THE BOMBS ARE BIGGER & THEY ARE OBEDIENT
& THEY PROVIDE THE END TO ALL THINGS, REFUGEES
INCLUDED).

③

THEN KASPER SAYS TO THE BAKER: PLEASE
ELABORATE, WHAT'S THE THANK-YOU OF THE REFUGEE KIDS?
& THE BAKER SAYS: THAT'S WHAT IT IS = THANK YOU.
IT'S CUSTOMARY, THEY DON'T
WANT TO EXACTLY, THEY JUST
SAY IT. & KASPER: BUT THEIR
ANKLES ARE BLOODIED & THE
BAKER REPLIES = THAT'S A GOOD KIND OF BLOOD, IT'S
LITTLE IT'S A BAREFOOTERS COMMON FARE, IT SAYS TO
THE BAREFOOTER: YOU ARE NOT A SHOE, YOU ARE A
CAT OR A FOX MAYBE, YOU ARE PART OF WHAT YOU
ADMIRE, BECAUSE BAREFOOTERS HAVE 1 FOOT IN THE
ANIMAL KINGDOM & CONCERNING REFUGEES, NOBODY
CAN EVER BE NOT A REFUGEE ANYWAY, ALL THIS CONSTANT
FLEEING, THE EVERYDAY RUNNING FROM THIS & THAT
THE STORMS, THE KISSES, THE DADDIES & ACCIDENTS, ALL
THIS INVOLUNTARY REFUGEEDOM, WHO CAN EVER AVOID
BEING A REFUGEE. AND YET THE EXTREME REFUGEE
WHOSE LIFE IS REFUGEE IS THE CLEAREST. HIS LIFE
LOST HUMAN HISTORY & STARTS UP AGAIN BARREN
WITHOUT HISTORY. TIME IS UP SAYS THE BAKER.
OFF WE GO SAYS KASPER

BUT BUT BUT BUT BUT SAYS THE GRANDPA, WITH THE ORIENTATIONDEPARTMENT IMBALANCE, EXCESSIVE REFUGEEDOM IS NATIONALLY & INTERNATIONALLY IMPERMISSIBLE BECAUSE IT'S NOT PERMITTED & THEREFORE STRICTLY FORBIDDEN YOU CAN'T HAVE IT NEITHER HERE NOR THERE NOR ANY- WHERE SAYS THE LAW & HOW CAN BE WHAT IS NOT ALLOWED TO BE SAYS GRANDPA, BUT BELLS ARE RINGING NOW NOW NOW FOR THE SHERIFFS' FUNERAL. DID THE SHERIFF SHERIFF ENOUGH? WAS HE CHOSEN FOR EXCELLENCE BY THE FUNERAL PARLOR? DID THE PREACHER NEED HIM EXPLICITLY FOR HIS SERMON? EVERYTHING

UNDER THE SUN IS EXACTLY AS IT IS & SHOULD ALSO BE EXACTLY AS IT IS. THE STUFF THAT BLOWS UP YOUR HOUSE & THROWS YOUR KIDS INTO THE FURNACE & THE STUFF THAT BLESSES YOUR KID'S BIRTHDAYPARTY WITH PIZZA & LOLLIPOPS & THE MIGHTY LOVERS WITH THEIR REDHOT EMBRACE & THE CONSEQUENT SUPER- BABIES WITH THEIR ROSY SUPERCOMPLEXION & THE SLAUGHTERERS OF THAT, ALL GET THEIR ALLOCATED PERFORMANCE IN THE SPECTACLE WHICH IS FOREVER THE SAME FOR THE PLEASURE OF THE AUTHOR PREACHES THE PREACHER, HOLY COW, PLEASE LEAVE FOREVER EVERYTHING THE SAME, BECAUSE EVERYTHING IS ALREADY O.K. BEFORE IT EVEN HAPPENS PREACHES THE PREACHER:

⑤

TO MAKE THE BEST USE OF THE SHERIFF'S
FUNERAL PARLORISATION. & THE WISE ATTENDANTS
NOD THEIR APPROVALHEADS & THE SENSE OF THE
SHERIFF'S DEATH PLUS THE SENSE OF THE REST OF
EVERYTHINGELSE IS SUDDENLY ESTABLISHED
& THE ATTENDANTS SLIDE OBEDIENTLY THROUGH
THE EXITS WHERE A PROFANE SUN BRIGHTENS
THE HOLY SNOW

IN THE MEANTIME THE GOD OF DITCHES SUFFERS
A FIT OF SPRING FEVER WITH ALL THE TEE-TEE-TEE-
TEEVIT-TA-TA-TA-TAA & TRA-RI-RA-LALAS & THE
WILD & THE DOMESTICATED TURKEY DANCES & THE
COONS' SHOW OF FORCE BRAVING THE DEADLY PAVEMENT
(WITHOUT THE FUNERALIZED SHERIFF EVEN MORE SO)
& THE PREACHER'S SERMON GAINS MOMENTUM
WITH ALL THE COON KIDS' JOLLY BIRTHDAY PARTIES
FOLLOWED BY RANDOM MASSACRES BY THE VORACIOUS
TRAFFIC & THE GOD OF DITCHES AS HELPLESS AS ANY
GOD SNEEZES HIS SPRINGSNEEZES & IS FOGGY FOR
⑥

A WHILE WHICH HELPS TO SLOW DOWN THE CARS &
THEN PRACTICES HIS FAMOUS PEEPER SONG, THE
ULTIMATE BATTLESONG OF SPRING'S DIRTY WAR
AGAINST WINTER. NOT YET THOUGH, NOT QUITE,
WAIT A LITTLE, PATIENCE PLEASE. GET THE SUGAR-
BUSH INTO YOUR BOOTS, BOIL & BOIL A LITTLE SAP SAP
SAP, CHOP A LITTLE WOOD WOOD WOOD. THE SUGAR-
BUSH CHIRPS ALREADY & FRIENDLINESS IS JUST
AROUND THE CORNER. ANYWAY, THE PEOPLE
WITH THE LIFE-IN-THE-DITCHES PHILOSOPHY AREN'T
NECESSARILY GOOD PROMOTIONAL AGENTS, LIKE
THE REST OF CIVILIZATION. THEY FOREVER SUFFER
ALL KIND OF CONSEQUENCES. THEY DITCH THEMSELVES

FOR VARIOUS REASONS WITH
VARIOUS DEGREES OF BELOW-
MINIMUM-WAGE-SURVIVAL-
CAPABILITY. THEY WANT &
THEY WANT NOT. THEY PRETEND &
THEY ARE, WHICH IS NOT TO SAY THEY ARE
DISHONEST, OR, IF SO, MUCH LESS SO THAN THE
CIVILIZATION THAT SQUEEZES THEM. DITCHING IS
NOT A SPORT, BUT A WAY OF SITTING INDEPENDENT
& INDEPENDENCE-BEYOND-BELIEF IS WRITTEN ON THE
SITTERS' SHIRTSLEEVES. YOU GUESS YOUR WAY INTO
SUBSTANDARD TRAVAILS & JOYS. SEVERAL LITTLENESSES
COURAGEOUSLY AVOID THE GENERAL BIGNESS.

⑦

OH YOU SNOW! COVER THE BROWN EARTH & COOL THE
MAPLES. LITTLE CHUNKS OF ICE PROTECT THE SAP FROM
FERMENTATION. THE PATHS ARE SUFFICIENTLY WORN.
YOU SELDOM BREAK THROUGH THE CRUST — PUT THE MAUL
TO WORK CHOP CHOP CHOP. KEEP THE FIRE HAPPY HALLELUJAH.
IF YOU'RE LUCKY THE PILEATED WOODPECKER WILL PLAY HIS
DRUM FOR YOU TUCK TUCK TUCK. OH YOU SNOW!
LANDLORD OF THE NORTHEAST KINGDOM.

THE TREES SPEAK WIND LANGUAGE. THE SOUTHWIND
PERFORMS HER SOPRANO SOLO. GRANDPA CHECK OUT
ALL THAT IS EARLY. THE OLD SHERIFF IS DEAD, BUT
NEW SHERIFFS GROW ALREADY TO TAKE HIS PLACE
THE UNEMPLOYED FUNERAL PARLOR HAS NOTHING TO
OFFER. THE HOUSES ARE EMPTY & DON'T SMELL, THE
T.V.s ARE ABANDONED. THE WIND BLOWS & SHE.
THE BEAUTY AMONG THE ICELANDIC EWES SUFFERED
A PROLAPSED UTERUS & HAS TO BE BUTCHERED &
HER FACE LOOKS AT US AS SHE GETS CUT UP
FOR THE FREEZER. OH YOU SNOW!

25

26

BREAD&PUPPET
PRESS 2007

BREAD & PUPPET

KASPER 17

SNOW

KASPER YIELDS KIDS & GRANDPA. GRANDPA IS ALSO
ASSISTANT SNOWMAN-ARCHITECT OF CLASSICAL
SNOWMAN IMPROVEMENT OF MAN. APRIL SNOW HOLDS
BACK THE SAP IN THE MAPLE TREES & MAKES THE THINKERS
THINK. ORLANDO FURIOSO HAS ARRIVED FROM THE MIDDLE
AGES WITH SWORD & SHIELD, 8 YEARS DANGEROUS, OH
YOU SNOW! WILSON BENTLEY, VERMONT'S SNOW FLAKE
ARCHIVIST MUST RECORD MILLIONS OF PRISTINE WORLDS
FALLING ON THE EXISTING COW: THE FAT WORLD & WHILE
THE FAT WORLD GROANS & MOANS UNDER THE WEIGHT
OF ITS CREAKING MACHINERY THE GREAT WHITE
TOSSES THE UNHOLY WORLD BACK INTO ITS HOLY
ORIGIN.

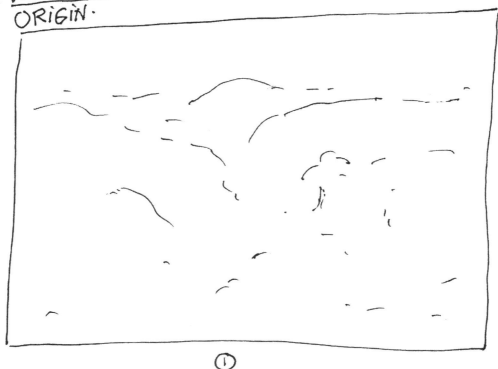

1

31

OH YOU SNOW! GOD OF THE EXTERIOR WHICH ALL RESIDENT SOULS NEED MORE THAN THEIR OWN SUFFERING INTERIORS. THE PARTICULAR INTERIOR IN QUESTION IS A GOD-FORLORN MESS, AN EXACT REPLICA OF ITS OCCUPANTS' INTERIOR, EXHILARATED BY THE WORKERS, THE UNTAMEABLE MESS MAKERS, ALSO RELATIONSHIPS OF SNOW, GRANDCHILDREN. THE SPRINGSNOW SUFFOCATES THE TRA-RI-RA-LA-LAS & THE MESSMAKERS' SHRIEKS TAKE OVER: KITCHENSPRING, ROAMING WILD PLASTIC BEASTS & PERPETUAL FERTILITY DANCES OF MINIATURE FEET, UP & DOWN & UNDER & UP NON-STOP & THE GRANDMAS & THE GRANDPAS WRAP THEIR FACES IN LITTLE BITS OF SILENCE, YET UNSUCCESSFULLY WHO CARES. THE SNOW IS RISEN ON THIS DAY HALLELUJAH!

②

WHAT IS A THING ALL WHITE ON TOP & A TRUNK STICKS OUT AT THE BOTTOM? WHAT IS FLUFFY WHITE WITH MORE WHITE ON TOP & 4 LEGS UNDERNEATH? A CAR IS NICE BUT WHEN IT'S STUCK & DOESN'T GO ANYWHERE IT'S JUST LIKE ANYTHING ELSE. MANY MANY KASPERS HAVE ALREADY LIVED IN THE SNOW & HAVE ONLY TENTATIVELY SUCCEEDED TO MANAGE IT. EVEN THOUGH MANAGEMENT WAS ON THE TOP OF THEIR LIST OF ACHIEVEMENTS. ANTISNOW COATS & ROOFS HAVE BEEN INVENTED LONG AGO. THE FIERCE ELEMENTS HAVE LONG BEEN ROUGHHOUSED INTO SUBMISSION. THE MANAGERS' CHILDREN MOVE AROUND PROUDLY WITH INHERITED SENSE OF ACHIEVEMENT & INDEED CROWDS OF ACHIEVERS ACHIEVE EVER MORE PARAPHERNALIA & THEIR MESSMAKER KIDS CONTINUOUSLY DESTROY & RECONSTRUCT THE ACHIEVEMENTS WITH *PLUS THE CURES FOR THE ILL EFFECTS OF THE PARAPHERNALIA* THE HELP OF PLASTIC IMITATION PARA- PHER NALIA, HOORAH! HOORAH! HOORAH!

③

ANOTHER SNOW, ANOTHER STRATEGY MEETING
ANOTHER SNOWBALLFIGHT & EASTER, SANTA EXECUTED
& RESURRECTED, HE WHO TEASES THE MASSES WITH HIS
COMMUNIST COSTUME, A JOLLY GOOD FELLOW UNTIL HE
SEES THE NEED TO BE THE OPPOSITE OF A JOLLY GOOD
FELLOW, NEVERTHELESS RESURRECTED BY EASTER EGGS
REAL & IRREAL, RED & BLUE HALLELUJAH. & FROM SANTA
ISSUE THE SANTA MISSION DANCERS WITH EQUAL POLITICAL
ZEAL, LUMPY BODIES WITH AN ANIMALISTIC AESTHETIC
WHICH MEANS UNPHOTOGENIC, IMMATURE WITHOUT THE
ASSOCIATED HANDSOME FEATURES. THEY PROMOTE ETERNAL
XMAS WITH JINGLEBELLS & GLITTERGARBAGE & THE LOVELY
FRENZY OF NON-STOP SHOPPING AS A NEW WAY OF LIFE
SUSTAINED BY THE FASTEST PIZZAPIES & FINEST DISHWATER
COFFEES AS DESIRED BY THE DEEPLY RELIGIOUS MERCANTILE
SYSTEM THAT SUSTAINS US ALL, US, THE PRETTY ONES WITH
THE PSYCHIATRISTS. THE SUPERGRANDPA ABOVE LOVES THE
EVERYTHING INCLUSIVE DEMOLITION & TORTURE BECAUSE OF
ITS EVERYTHING & SANTA IS THE DISTRIBUTION FATSO.

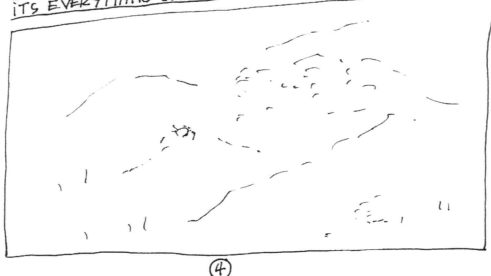

④

34

NOW THAT THE LOGIC OF THE WHOLE THING IS OUT, THE
SANTA MISSION DANCERS DANCE THE LOGIC TO ITS HEAD
WITH THE ASSISTANCE OF THEIR KNEES IN 100 KNEE
DANCES HALLELUJAH. THE SNOW IS RISEN ON THIS DAY
HALLELUJAH. GIVE ME A BREAK SAYS GRANDMA.
OH SHIT SAYS GRANDPA & NOW SHUT UP TILL THE SUN
CRACKS OPEN THE GREY. THE MESSMAKER KIDS NEED
TO TASTE SNOW ON THEIR LIPS. THEIR BOOTS RATTLE
THE DOOR & INVADE THE SNOW FOR NOTHING AT ALL
& THEY DROWN IN IT MANY TIMES. BEAN SOUP & DRY
PANTS FRESH FROM THE WOODSTOVE FOR LUNCH. THE
ACORN WOODPECKER WORKS THE SUET.

⑤

WHAT'S MISSING? THE MESSMAKERS NEED DRUMS BADLY & DRUMS NEED TO BE EXCAVATED FROM THEIR STORAGE DEN. DRUMTIME NEEDS TO FASTEN THE LITTLE GROWN-UPS TO THEIR SEATS. DRUMCLOCKS STRETCH THE DAY. THE FURNITURE PICKS UP THE BEAT. KITCHEN WARE BEWARE! AS THE HUMANOIDS COOK UP THEIR EASTERFEAST FROM LAMB & COLLARD GREENS & GARLIC & THE EASTERWORLD THINKS OF ITS DIGNIFIED PAST WHICH IT DOESN'T KNOW ANY MORE, BUT IT DREAMS AS IF THERE WAS MORE TO IT & THE KIDS' DRUMS & THE GARLIC ALERT KEEP THE EASTERMONSTER IN CHECK SINCE THE BUNNYRABBITS ARE ALL BOILED DOWN TO NOTHING & THE RECITALS OF THE TIME HONORED MAGNIFICENCE DON'T PENETRATE THE SKIN — ONLY THE VERITABLE MAGNIFICAT DOES LONG DESIGNATED RIVER OF THE EARS ROARING THE MAGNIFICENCE.

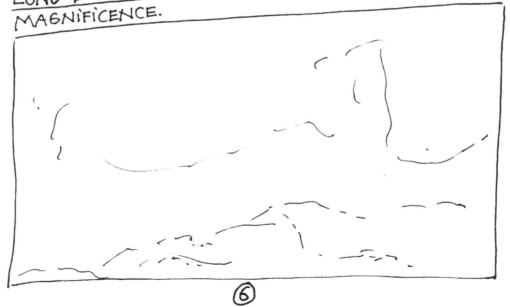

⑥

BACK TO THE SANTA MISSION DANCERS & THEIR
GLORIFICATIONS. CAN THEY RIDE OUT THE EASTER SNOW?
CAN THEY EXTRACT PANCAKE SYRUP FROM TREES & YET
SHAME THE POLITICAL FATSOS? CAN THEY RECRUIT THE
NECESSARY HOBBY HORSE ELEMENTS FOR IMMINENT
ATTACK? CAN THEY GLORIFY BOTH ATTACK & SYRUP
SUFFICIENTLY TO ACHIEVE MEANINGFUL POPULAR ADDRESS?
CAN THEY AROUSE THE DOOMED LANDSCAPE FULL OF
DESTABILIZED CREATURES? CAN THEY DANCE HARD
& LONG ENOUGH TO GET ANYWHERE? WHAT IS
THEIR FINAL DESTINATION? IS IT POSSIBLE TO DANCE
THE SHIT OUT OF THINGS AS THEY DESERVE IT?
WHAT ARE THE WEATHER PREDICTIONS? IF THIS IS
SPRING WHAT IS WINTER LIKE ANYWAY? IT'S EASTER
BUT THE POST EASTER REALITY ALREADY LASHES
OUT AT US. BEWARE MISSION DANCERS, UPRIGHT YOURSELVES!

⑦

THE NEXT QUESTIONS CONCERN THE MESSMAKERS.
HOW SHALL THEY GROW UP & OUT? HOW SHALL THEIR
GROWING BE RIGHT? WHAT WILL THE WEATHER BE?
WHAT CHANCES DO THE MESSES HAVE IN THE
SIMULATED HARMONY? WHICH PITCHES FOR THEIR
SHRIEKS? WHAT CULTURE FOR THEIR DRUMS?
THE CAT PLAYS WITH THE DEATHTHROES OF A WILD
PILLOW & THE MESSMAKERS LEARN DEATHPLAY. THEY NEVER
FINISH. THEY NEVER START EITHER. THEY ALWAYS HIT THE
MIDDLE ~ ONLY NOW IN THE SNOW CAN THEY BE WHAT
THEY ARE & EVENTUALLY NO MORE. THEIR FURTHER
BEING IS NORMALIZED IN THE READYMADE EVERYTHING.
BRIGHT FUTURES ARE ALREADY FIGURED OUT FOR THEM
BY FUTURISTIC LEGISLATIONS.

⑧

&THEN THE ONES LEFT BEHIND, SNOWSUFFERERS, UNEMPLOYED KNEES, EX-ELYSIUM DANCERS, THUNDERERS, BATTLETIRED JUVENILES &THEIR SUPERVISORS, WORN OUT &RETARDED PHILOSOPHERS, HOW WILL THEY GET UP FROM UNDERNEATH THE LATE SNOW? WHAT UNMOTORIZED SPEEDS & RAW FORCES ARE AVAILABLE TO THEM? CAN THEY SALVAGE FRAGMENTS OF SHRIEKS & SNOWBALLFIGHTS FOR CONSTRUCTIVE PURPOSES? WHAT ARE THE CONSTRUCTIVE PURPOSES? UNBUILT DWELLINGS WITH UNELECTRIFIED LIVES IN THEM? UNRECLAIMED DUMPS WHERE THE FORGOTTEN TORSOS ARE? WHERE IS LIFE?

⑨

ON THE LAST PAGE THE KIDS ARE HUNGRY AGAIN.
GO TO THE HORSEFARM WHERE THEY HAVE RAW MILK
FROM JOYCE THE COW & HER HANDSOME SON STANDS
NEXT TO HER. HAIRPULLING & OTHER TRAGEDIES ARE
FINISHED. NIGHTCOLD SETTLES IN.

BREAD&PUPPET
PRESS 2007

BREAD & PUPPET

KASPER 18

GOD

45

47

49

HUMAN HISTORY IS A MONSTER & IS THEREFORE
A MONSTROUS HUMAN HISTORY & IF I REGISTER
A GOD WHO BECAUSE OF WHO HE IS, IS THE
INSPIRER & CONDONER OF THE MONSTROUS
HISTORY O LA-LA-LA-LA PEOPLE WOULD
PRODUCE POLITICS & PARTIES & EDUCATION
& STUPIFICATION ALL CLAIMING TO BE ISSUED
BY THE MONSTROUS HUMAN LIKENESS &
THEY WOULD BUILD SPECIAL CLUBS & HOUSES
& FESTIVITIES & THEY WOULDN'T EVEN KNOW
THAT THEY LIVE & DIE BECAUSE THEY WOULD
BLAME IT ALL ON HIM & THEY WOULD SAY:
EVERYTHING IS FINE AS IT IS, EVERYTHING
HAS ITS TIME, GENTLENESS & TORTURE, WAR
WHICH IS CALLED WAR & WAR WHICH IS
CALLED PEACE & ALL WOULD BE FULL OF

⑥

O LA-LA-LA

⑨

53

BREAD&PUPPET
PRESS 2007
GLOVER VT

BREAD & PUPPET

KASPER 19

THE POLITICALLY CORRECT SNOW WHITE-OUT COVERS UP ALL MISTAKES

THE HORSES ARE READY & THE SWORDS ARE SHARPENED

THE SECRETARY OF DEFENSE ORDERS MORE TROOPS

①

60

CAN MORE TROOPS

BE SAVED FROM DYING

AND

THE

CONGRESS

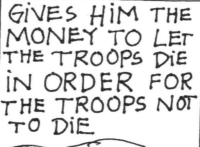

GIVES HIM THE MONEY TO LET THE TROOPS DIE IN ORDER FOR THE TROOPS NOT TO DIE

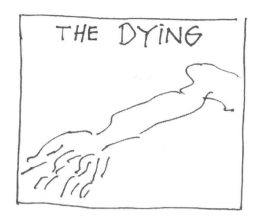

& THE PRESIDENT WATCHES ON THE NEWS HOW THE DEMOCRACIZED PEOPLE

BLOW EACH OTHER

UP

& HE DECIDES THEY ARE NOT DEMOCRACIZED ENOUGH

& THEY NEED A DIFFERENT KIND OF BLOWING UP WHICH IS MUCH MORE EXPENSIVE

& THEN HE POURS A LOT OF MONEY ON THE WHOLE THING

& THEN THE BLOWING UP IS MUCH MORE GIGANTIC.

⑥

64

65

& THE SPECIALIST SAYS: THIS IS A

VERY DANGEROUS SITUATION

ESPECIALLY BECAUSE OF IRAN & AS THE PRESIDENT SAYS WE

NEED DEMOCRATIC NON-VIOLENT SOLUTIONS

& THEREFORE WE MUST GIVE MORE MONEY TO ISRAEL

⑨

THAT IT CAN PROTECT ITSELF WITH ATOMIC BOMBS

BREAD & PUPPET
PRESS 2007

BREAD & PUPPET

KASPER 20

THE ETHICAL CLEANING CORPORATION

CLEANING FACILITIES ALSO DIFFER ENORMOUSLY ACCORDING TO THE TASK AT HAND

CLEANING OF BATTLEGEAR IS DONE BY WASHING MACHINES. CLEANING OF CITIES REQUIRES NOT ONLY GROUNDFORCES BUT ALSO MASSIVE AIR SUPPORT

⑦

79

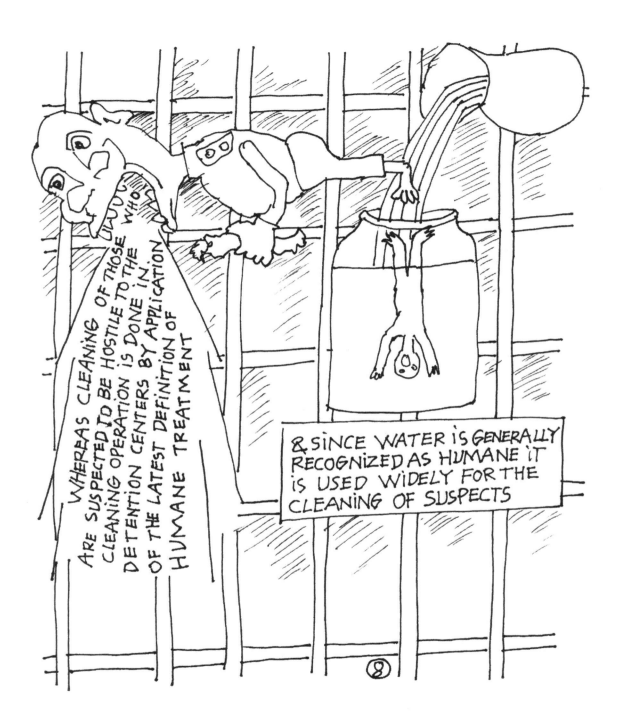

WHEREAS CLEANING OF THOSE WHO ARE SUSPECTED TO BE HOSTILE TO THE CLEANING OPERATION IS DONE IN DETENTION CENTERS BY APPLICATION OF THE LATEST DEFINITION OF HUMANE TREATMENT

& SINCE WATER IS GENERALLY RECOGNIZED AS HUMANE IT IS USED WIDELY FOR THE CLEANING OF SUSPECTS

THE HARDER THE ETHICAL CLEANING CORPORATION WORKS THE MORE NEEDS TO BE DONE IF THE WORLD IS TO BE CLEAN BY THE HIGH STANDARDS OF THE ETHICAL CLEANING CORPORATION

⑨

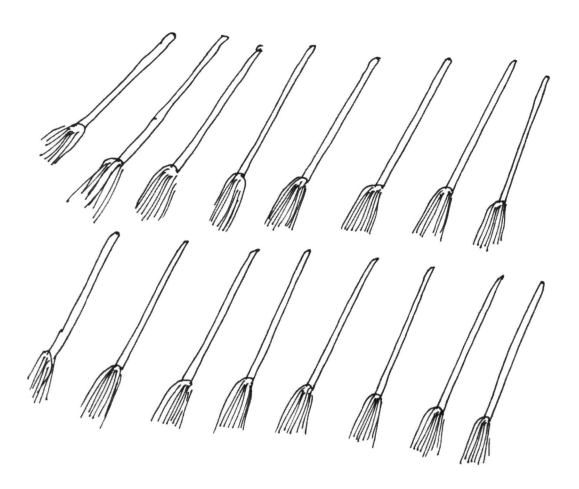

THERE IS NO END IN SIGHT

⑩

BREAD&PUPPET
PRESS 2007
GLOVER VT

BREAD & PUPPET

KASPER 21

FOREIGN AFFAIRS

KASPER NEEDS A JOB

HE GETS ONE FROM THE DIGESTION DEPARTMENT

THANK YOU

TO MAKE PHOTOS OF CURRENT AFFAIRS & TO MAKE THEM DIGESTABLE, FOR EXAMPLE LIKE SAUSAGES

FOR A HUNGRY POPULATION

FIRST YOU TAKE A COURSE IN DIGESTABILITY

IT'S A VERY NICE COURSE & YOU GET TO EAT A LOT

87

SECOND, YOU LEARN RUNNING

BECAUSE THE CURRENTS ARE VERY FAST & THE AFFAIRS ALSO

NEXT IT'S AN UPHILL BATTLE

BECAUSE YOU HAVE TO BE THERE BEFORE THE OTHERS

TA-TA!

FOR EXAMPLE: THE MOMENT WHEN GOD PUTS THE PRESIDENT ON THE WARHORSE

IT'S A VERY DIFFICULT HORSE & ONLY WITH THE HELP OF GOD CAN THIS BE DONE

②

89

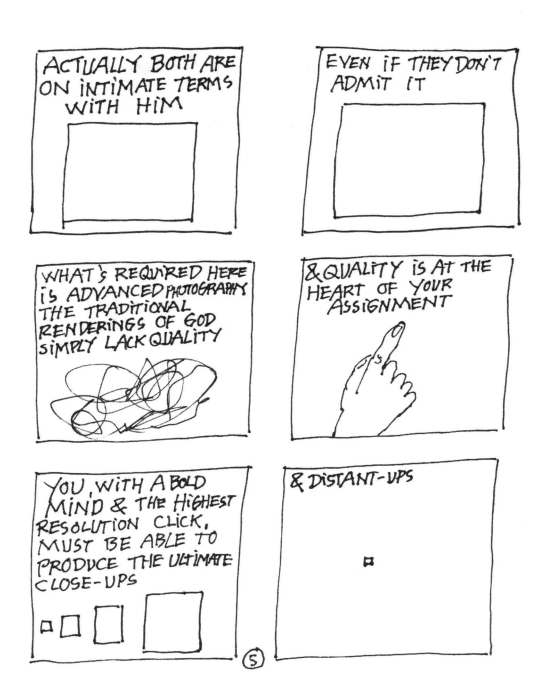

ACTUALLY BOTH ARE ON INTIMATE TERMS WITH HIM

EVEN IF THEY DON'T ADMIT IT

WHAT'S REQUIRED HERE IS ADVANCED PHOTOGRAPHY THE TRADITIONAL RENDERINGS OF GOD SIMPLY LACK QUALITY

& QUALITY IS AT THE HEART OF YOUR ASSIGNMENT

YOU, WITH A BOLD MIND & THE HIGHEST RESOLUTION CLICK, MUST BE ABLE TO PRODUCE THE ULTIMATE CLOSE-UPS

& DISTANT-UPS

⑤

& WITHIN THESE (STILL EXTREMELY EDIBLE) IMAGES

ARE CONTAINED ALL POSSIBLE ENTERTAINMENT & INFORMATION VALUES, REQUIRED BY YOUR CLIENTELE

YOUR HIGHLY EDUCATED & WELLTRAINED DEMOCRACY

& PROBABLY THE CONSUMPTION OF YOUR IMAGES WILL RESULT IN EVEN FASTER CURRENTS & AFFAIRS

WITH EVER MORE HEROIC CONCLUSIONS

⑥

AGAIN & AGAIN

TILL ONE DAY

YOU LOSE YOUR JOB

BECAUSE THE CURRENTS & THE AFFAIRS ARE NO LONGER ACCESSIBLE TO ANY IMAGRY

BUT ARE OFF ON THEIR OWN

& THE PHOTOGRAPHERS ARE ALL FLATTENED OUT LIKE PANCAKES

⑦

& THEIR CLIENTELES ARE EVEN FLATTER

& THE CLOSEST CLOSE-UP OF GOD

LIES LIKE SNOW ON THE WORLD

& NOTHING DARES TO STIR ANYMORE

⑧

95

BREAD&PUPPET
PRESS 2007
GLOVER VT.

BREAD & PUPPET

KASPER 22

SCHNAPS

KASPER HAS A THOUGHT

A THOUGHT ISN'T A VISITATION OR A HOLY SPIRIT OR SOMETHING LIKE THAT. A THOUGHT IS A FABRICATION FROM THE GUTS OF THE ANIMAL THAT ROAMS IN THE BRAIN OF THE THINKER. THE THINKER MAY SMOKE A CIGAR OR HAVE A SCHNAPS & LOOK PERFECTLY PEACE-FUL. BUT HE REALLY IS AN OBSESSED & ANIMAL-ISTIC WARRIOR WHO PUSHES TOUGH LITTLE EXCERPTS OF HIMSELF & THEN FABRICATES THOUGHT FROM THIS STUFF. A TORNADO IN A SCHNAPSGLASS. 100 MILE WINDS QUIVER THE NOSTRILS & PENETRATE THE CONFUSED PART OF THE BRAIN & FORCE RESULTS. ACTUALLY RESULTS ARE RIDICULOUS! NO, THOUGHT IS NOT A RESULT. IT'S JUST A PIECE OF WIND, AN EVAPORATING CHUNK, RIPPED FROM THE GENERIC SOMETHING, UNTIL FINALLY, AFTER SO MUCH WIND, IT RESULTS IN A RESULT. WHEN THE SCHNAPS IS GONE & THE CIGAR IS ASHES, KASPER NEEDS TO WATCH THE RAVENS ON THE COMPOSTPILE & HE QUICKLY PICKS UP A DIRT-DIGGING LESSON FOLLOWED BY A TAKE-

①

FLIGHT LESSON FROM THE AWESOME BIRDS.
THEN HIS FACE TURNS BLACK LIKE A RAVEN! **AND HE TEARS** HIS SHIRT INTO SHREDS! **AND HE** CAWS THE RAVEN CAW! **AND HE SHOUTS:** WE MUST FORM A STRATEGY HOW TO ATTACK THE SHIT! **WHAT** DO WE NEED? **HOW** DO WE NEED IT? (THIS QUESTION WHIPS HIS LEGS & MAKES HIM RUN TWICE AROUND THE ROOM.) THEN HE FALLS FLAT ON HIS FACE & HE SINGS: OH-LA-LA-LA.

②

KASPER RECONSIDERS

NATURALLY SOON AFTER, A LITTLE DIZZY FROM THE SCHNAPS & A LITTLE ITCHY ABOUT THE TORN-UP SHIRT, KASPER HAS SECOND THOUGHTS ABOUT HIS THOUGHT. HE TURNS INTO THE NORMAL DAYLIGHT FOR ITS CHICKEN-BUSINESS & ITS PHONE CALLS & HE GIVES HIS THOUGHT THE COLD-WATER-TREATMENT & MESSES WITH THE RESULT & INSULTS IT & BEHAVES LIKE ANY ORDINARY IDIOT & PULLS OUT HIS TAPE MEASURE & MEASURES THE DISTANCE FROM THE COMPOSTPILE TO THE WINDOW & TURNS ON THE RADIO & LISTENS TO THE LATEST EXPLOSION IN IRAQ. & MORE & MORE IT LOOKS LIKE HE IS TRYING TO GET OUT FROM UNDER HIS THOUGHT. HE NEEDS TO CHEW A SLICE OF BLACK BREAD WITH GARLIC & CHEESE & CONSEQUENTLY HE PICKS A FIGHT WITH NOBODY, A STANDARD FIGHT, SWINGING HIS ARMS SENSELESSLY. THAT'S IT. HE IS STUCK. WHAT DOES IT TAKE TO UNSTICK HIM?

KASPER WASHES THE DISHES

THEN HE MIGHT AS WELL WASH DISHES, WHY NOT?
SUBMITTING TO THE HUMDRUM MISSION • AN EN-
LIGHTENED EVERYDAY SPORT WHICH KEEPS YOU
IN SHAPE LIKE NOTHING ELSE • FURTHERMORE
IT DOESN'T COST ANYTHING & MAKES YOUR HEART
BEAT IN THIRD DOMESTIC-HAPPINESS GEAR PLUS THE
HAPPINESS OF YOUR WIFE'S BRAVO ~ BRAVISSIMO •
ALMOST AS GOOD AS EATING MINUS THE TASTEBUDS •
TICKLED BY WARM SOAPWATER & MORAL SUPERI-
ORITY • MAMA MIA!

④

MUD SEASON

BUSINESS CLOUDS OVER ANCIENT LAUNDRY-
LINE WHICH THE WIND BURSTS INTO LAUGHTER,
HOPPING TO & FRO TILL THE TURKEYS JOIN IN.
THE WIND GETS INTO THE SHEEP, CATCHES THE
PREGNANT EWE & AS THE LAUNDRY LAUGHS
ITS SILLY LAUGHTER, SHE BRINGS FORTH HER
FIRST BORN ONE & THEN ANOTHER & THE WIND
STROKES THEIR MATCHSTICK LEGS & THE LAMBS
SNEEZE THEIR FIRST HOLY SNEEZE BECAUSE ALL
IS RISEN, ALL, ALL, ALL, THE EWE & HER LAMBS,
THE CURIOUS CHICKEN, THE SNOW ON THE COMPOST-
PILE, ALL, ALL, ALL, THE MUD IN THE ROAD, BECAUSE
IT IS THE HALLELUJAH-THE-MUD SEASON, ALL, ALL,
ALL, THE KIDS, EVEN THOUGH THEY ARE NOT HERE,
THE CATS FOR SURE.

⑤

PUMMELING

WE NEED TO PUMMEL THE SHIT, SAYS KASPER.
DO YOU HAVE PUMMELING EQUIPMENT TO PUMMEL
THE HEADBUSTING TECHNOLOGY? DO YOU HAVE
HORSES LIKE GHENGIS KHAN OR OTHERWISE
HOBBYHORSES? AND EVEN PUMMELERS CAN BE
INVENTED. WHAT'S NEEDED IS THEIR FIERCE SPIRIT
WHICH THEY CALL GHENGIS KHAN. WE HAVE TO
THROW A NON-EXISTING WARRIOR STYLE, COMPRISED
OF SHITKICKING HEARTS, RIGHT INTO THE FACE
OF THE SHIT, LIKE THE GRAND OLD DUKE OF
YORK WITH HIS 5000 UPHILLERS & DOWNHILLERS
& EVEN HALF-WAY-UPPERS. AND THE HOBBYHORSE
CAVALRY IS THE EXTENTION OF THE WILDERNESS
IN THE MINDS OF THE ATTACKERS. IS IT THE
CAPITALIST SHIT OR WHICH OR THE MODERNITY
MONSTER WITH ITS OFFICE OF PROFESSIONAL
RESPONSIBILITY IN CHARGE OF HUMAN RESOURCES?
WITH ALL THE POTATOES I GROW IN MY LITTLE
NOTHING-MUCH GARDEN, NEVER DO I SEE HUMANS
AMONGST MY POTATOES. WHY? DON'T THEY
REALIZE THEIR RELATIONSHIP, AT LEAST THE
GREEN ONES SHOULD! I MYSELF, SPEAKING FOR
MY RELATIVES THE POTATOES, I PRONOUNCE THE
JOYOUS SCIENCE OF THE HOLY POTATO RELATION-
SHIP. YES, BECAUSE I AM A SHIP. A SHIP
FULL OF OTHERS & EQUIPPED WITH SAILS TO
FLEE THE FASCIST DEMOCRACY & HEADING

⑥

TOWARDS NOWHERE. & THE NOWHERE IS SWEET
LIKE MAPLE SYRUP, ONLY NO PANCAKES & NO
EATING. AM I PERHAPS SICK? OR SO FULL OF
NO-SICKNESS-AT-ALL THAT I MUST UPRISE IN
MY GUTS ALL THE TIME, THAT I CAN'T SIT IN
THE MUFFLED CORNER OF MY STUPID YEARS, SO
MANY OF THEM WITHOUT ANY EDUCATION &
EVEN SINCERE IN THEIR OPPOSITION TO SENSE.
OH PUMMELERS, WHERE ARE YOU LOCATED?
YOUR CARDBOARD HELMETS ARE READY. YOUR
MISSION IS WELL-COOKED, YOUR ATTACK
LOGICAL THOUGH YOUR STRATEGY IS UNKNOWN.
PUMMELERS YOU MUST OVERTHROW THE
GOVERNMENT. THE SHIT IS ON TOP OF US &
CLOGS OUR SOUL'S PLUMBING SYSTEM. THE
SUPERSHIT THAT PRETENDS ALL THE TIME &
AFFORDS UNIVERSITIES OF PRETENDING. &
THE IDEA IS THAT THE HOBBY-HORSE-RIDING
PUMMELERS MUST BURST THE BUBBLE IN
THE BRAIN OF THE PRETENDERS. & THEN
WHAT? JUST IMAGINE: WHAT THEN?

⑦

KASPER LOOKS FOR HIS MEGAPHONE

WHERE IS MY MEGAPHONE? WHO IS MY SPEECHWRITER TO WRITE THE EXACT ADDRESS TO THE NOT-YET PUMMELERS? TO ALL OF THEM SITTING AT THEIR OVERSENSITIVE DESKS IN THE MIDDLE OF THINGS, MASSES OF SLIGHTLY DERANGED INNOCENTS WITH NEVERTHELESS ENORMOUS PUMMELER TALENTS IF THEY'D ONLY THINK OF IT. WE MUST DIG THEM OUT FROM UNDER THE SURFACES, SINCE THEY THEMSELVES ARE AFRAID OF THE SURFACES & DON'T LIKE TO BE STASHED AWAY FOREVER & EVER. I PERSONALLY HAVE STOPPED TO BE STASHED AWAY, EVEN THOUGH NOT TOTALLY. NATURALLY I FEEL THE SPRINGTIME IN MY KNEES & I ARGUE WITH MY OWN PRIVATE OFFICE OF PROFESSIONAL RESPONSIBILITY. MY TIME IS UP. MY SPEECH IS NOT WRITTEN. THOUSANDS ARE HIDING IN THE MOST COMMON HIDING PLACES. NOTHING WILL EVER BE COMPLETE & THE HIDDEN FORCES IN THE INCOMPLETE COMMON PLACES MUST BE SUMMONED. LET'S GET BACK TO THE BEGINNING. DESIGN THE HOBBYHORSE CAVALRY.

⑧

NO MEGAPHONE YET

BEFORE DESIGNING ANYTHING, KASPER IS ON THE UPHILL GO, IN A BRISK MOOD, GESTURING HIS HANDS TOWARDS THE MASSES WHICH ARENT THERE, THEN SLOWS HIS PACE MOMENTARILY, THEN PRANCES A TYPICAL UPHILL DANCE, WHICH HE KNOWS IS SIMPLY CONTENTED FORWARDMOTION & CONSISTS OF RHYTHMICAL ARMSWINGS, INTERRUPTED BY A-SYMMETRICAL TWISTS OF THE TORSO. THE WIND PLAYS A BIG ROLE IN THE PERFORMANCE OF THE AFTERNOON. THE WIND WHICH JUST RECENTLY RAN THE WHOLE SHOW, IS NOT ITSELF ANYMORE. LUKEWARM CHAPTERS OF SOUTHERN AIR WIGGLE THE LANDSCAPE. THE RUSTBROWN CHICKENS WIGGLE ALSO. JUST A FEW HOURS AGO KASPER HAD GONE TO TOWN EXERCISING HIS GETTING- A- G-PACK DANCE RIGHT & NOW THIS. WHAT'S NEXT? DESIGNERTIME, EVEN OF HOBBYHORSES, IS NOT QUITE HERE YET. & YET, THE SOURDOUGH MUST KICK IN & KASPER IS SOUR, BUT PERHAPS NOT SOUR ENOUGH. & MEGAPHONES DON'T SLEEP, WITH ALL THE LYING AROUND THEY DO, THEY ARE INCREDIBLY SHARP & ABLEBODIED & EAGER TO TRANSFORM WHISPERS INTO MANIFESTOS.

(9)

109

KASPER STOPS

THE PROJECT IS NOT CLEAR YET & IT'S OF THE UTMOST IMPORTANCE TO NOT LEAVE ANYTHING OUT, BECAUSE WHAT IS OUT BOTHERS THE IN. DEFINITIONS ARE RICKETY, LANGUAGE UNAVAILABLE. HOBBYHORSES OR NOT, YOU MUST STICK WITH IT, SAYS KASPER. THE FORMERLY TRADITIONAL WOUNDS & OBSTACLES ARE NOW REGIMENTED. WITHIN 2 WEEKS OR 2 DECADES THE MILITARY WILL TAKE CHARGE OF THE AIR. BREATHING FACILITIES ARE STAKED OUT. THE FESTIVE SHOPPING CAPACITY OF THE ELECTORATE SHOPS DEMOCRACY. LIFE BLOSSOMS IN THE EXACTLY DESIRED RESTRICTIONS. A LAMB SEEMS TO BE LOST & CRIES FOR ITS MAMA.

BREAD & PUPPET
PRESS 2007
GLOVER VT

BREAD & PUPPET

KASPER 23

OVERWHELMING AMOUNTS OF
ARBITRARY LANDSCAPE, THE KIND
THAT MIXES UPS & DOWNS EASILY
& THWARTS THE TRAFFIC JUST
AS THE SKY THWARTS ITS
AIRPLANES. THE TRUCKS
TRY VERY HARD TO ROAR
THEIR MESSAGES WITHOUT
MEANING UNDER THE NOISY
GATHERING OF SPRINGWINDS
& BIRDS. THE TRUCKS SELDOM
STOP TO THINK IT OVER & SOON WILL BE REPLACED BY
BLACK FLIES. THE GLOBAL CARECONOMY TRICKLES
STEADILY DOWN THE SLOPES AS SO & SO MANY
ROT AWAY AT THE PLEASURE OF THE PRESIDENT.
HM—HM—HM—HM! A FEW GUNSHOTS SAY HI —
NOTHING NEW. THE WEATHER NEVER STOPS &
THROWS LIGHT AROUND THIS WAY & THAT WAY.
ONE MAN BLOWS HIS NOSE, ANOTHER PRACTICES
SITTING ON AN EARLY LAWNCHAIR. 2 BOYS CLIMB
INTO A TREEHOUSE ENVIED BY SQUIRRELS. AFTER—
NOON SHADOWS CRAWL OVER THINGS, OBLIVIOUS TO
THE CONSEQUENCES, IF THERE ARE ANY.

①

THE CAT'S MOUSING ISN'T GOING ANYWHERE.
QUITE A LISTENER SHE IS THOUGH. I'M NOT A
MOUSE, LUCKY ME, BUT NOT MUCH MORE EITHER.
THEY CALL IT A HIGHER FORM OF MOUSE, BUT THE
HIGH ISN'T VERY HIGH NOR DOES IT MAKE A
DIFFERENCE. WHATEVER LIFE i HAVE IS RELATED
TO BOTH CAT & MOUSE & ALSO TO THE TENSION
BETWEEN THE TWO.

IS IT WEDNESDAY? SOMEBODY ALWAYS
STEALS DAYS AROUND HERE OR IS IT
THE SAME ONE WHO STEALS YEARS?
THE SKY IS HERE. WHAT AM i GOING
TO DO WITH THIS MUCH SKY? HOW
CAN i STAND IT?

MAY BE
i COOK A SOUP

HE WHO SOUPS
LONG
LIVES LONG

BUT A SOUP IS JUST A SOUP & THE SKY
NEEDS SO MUCH MORE. & THE HORSES ARE
NOT READY. WHERE ARE MY HORSES? MANY
MANY MILES OF SKY ARE AHEAD OF US
②

& i DEPLORE THE ABSENCE OF THE HORSES.

BUT i HAVE NOT STARTED EVEN ON THE ADEQUATE PREPARATIONS OF THE PLANNING FOR THE COMPETENT THINKING ABOUT THE SUBJECT MATTER OF MY HORSES! THOSE WHOM YOU BRIDLE IN GREAT URGENCY

& DRIVE THEM THROUGH THE VAST GOVERN-
MENTAL VOID AS IF IT WASN'T THERE & RACE
THEM OVER THE HEADS OF CITIES AS IF THEY
WEREN'T THERE & NEVER STOP THEM, AS THEY
LAY WASTE TO THE PITIFUL LAND & BURN IT
WITH THEIR HOOVES.

THE VALLEY-BUSINESSMAKERS OF THE VALLEYS
& THE MOUNTAINTOP REMOVERS OF THE MOUNTAINS
& THE NON-POSSIBILITARIANS IN THE INDUSTRIAL
PARADISES CRUMBLE & THE VILLAGES TURN RED
& SPARKLE WITH FIREWORKS AS THE HORSES
GALLOP THROUGH THEIR DOORS & THE WINDOWS
OPEN WITH HUGE BIRDS JOINING A SQUADRON
OF BLACKBIRDS IN THE BLACK CLOUDS OF THE
THUNDERSTORM SKY.

⑤

& MANY BRASSBANDS WITH WILD TROMBONISTS
STAGGER OVER THE EARLY FIELDS & THE FIELDS
THOUGH NOT GREEN YET, ARE JOLLIER THAN YOU
HAVE EVER SEEN THEM & THERE IS NOBODY
LEFT ANYWHERE, BECAUSE THEY ARE ALL RUNNING
RUNNING & RUNNING WITH THE HORSES & THEY
ARE NOT WILLING TO STOP BECAUSE NOTHING
STOPS & EVEN THE NOTHING THAT STOPS DOESN'T
STOP & THE RUNNING RUNS & THE ENDLESS RUNNING
RUNS ENDLESSLY & FALLS & GETS UP & THEN IT
YELLS LIKE A SINGLE KID & LIKE A DOZEN KIDS
& THEN

⑥

TAKES A FEW LEAPS & THEN DROWNS & RUNS IN
THE RUNNING ·
& ALL THE MANY YEARS OF STUDIED STORMS ARE NOW
STORMS THEMSELVES & THEY CAN'T NOT BE STORMS
ANY LONGER & THIS IS THE TIME WHEN THE STORMS
TAKE OVER ALL THAT WAS NOT A STORM ·
BLUE SAILBOATS APPEAR IN THE MEADOWS · STORM
SINGERS SING NOTHING BUT STORM · SERIOUS
CONGREGATIONS SWIRL IN UNISON · HERDS OF WHITE
DEER PROCEED FROM THE PINE FORESTS · MARCHES
MARCH BRIGHT LIKE SUNLIGHT · THE FALLERS
FALL & GET UP, THE STUMBLERS STUMBLE ON, THE
CRAWLERS CRAWL & THE LAME INCH THEIR WAY
FORWARD AT INCREDIBLE SPEED · THE RIVERS
FLOW LIKE THE MASSES OF MOVERS, NOTHING
STOPS THEM, NOTHING WANTS TO, THE THINGS
ARE NOT STILL ANY LONGER, THE MOVERS MOVE
ALL THAT MOVES ·

121

BREAD&PUPPET
PRESS 2007
GLOVER VT

BREAD & PUPPET

KASPER 24

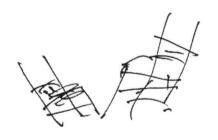

KASPER VISITS THE CHAIRS

CHAIRS GET ELECTED

TO BE CHAIRS

BY THE MEDIA

WHO TELL THE ELECTORATE

WHAT TO THINK &
WHOM TO ELECT
②

130

CHAIRS ARE PRESIDED OVER
BY THE CHAIRMAN WHO CAN
DO WHAT HE WANTS TO DO
UNLESS HE IS IMPEACHED
③

WHAT MAKES A CHAIR A CHAIR?

④

IN THE CHAIR SYSTEM THE
FUNCTION OF THE CHAIRS IS
NOT TO DO THINGS BUT TO
CHAIR THE DOING OF THINGS

⑤

IN THE THEATER OF WAR THE
CHAIRS PRESIDE OVER THREE
CATEGORIES OF WAR-FUNCTIONARIES

THE FIRST CATEGORY ARE
THE WARRIORS, WHOSE JOB
IS TO INFLICT CALAMITIES &
FATALITIES

THE SECOND CATEGORY ARE
THE VICTIMS WHO ARE DESIGNATED
TO SUFFER THE CALAMITIES + FATALITIES

⑥

& THE THIRD CATEGORY ARE THE PRISONERS WHO BEAR THE CONSEQUENCES OF BEING IN NEITHER CATEGORY.

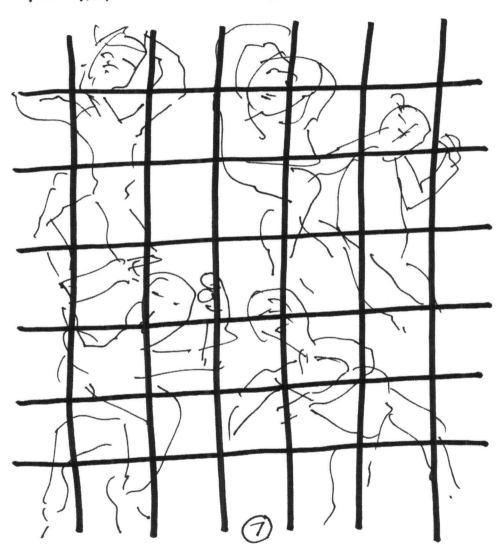

IN THE THEATER OF WAR THE
WARRIORS DIE AT THE PLEASURE
OF THE CHAIRS, WHICH MEANS
THE CHAIRS HAVE TO PAY FOR
THE WARRIORS' DEATHS EVEN
BEFORE THE WARRIORS DIE.
IF THE CHAIRS DON'T AGREE
WITH THE DEATHS OF THE
WARRIORS OR DON'T WANT
TO PAY FOR THE DEATHS OF
THE WARRIORS, THE CHAIRMAN
CAN OVERRIDE THEIR DIS-
AGREEMENT. IN THAT CASE
THE WARRIORS DIE AT THE
PLEASURE OF THE CHAIRMAN

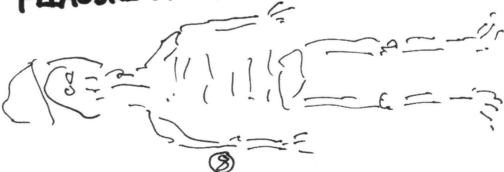

THE SECOND CATEGORY OF WAR-
FUNCTIONARIES, THE VICTIMS, ARE
LUCKILY FAR OUT OF SIGHT & THE
MEDIA HAVE AGREED NOT TO TAKE
THEIR PICTURES, THEREFORE THEIR
IMPORTANCE IS GREATLY DIMINISHED
& DOES NOT COME MUCH INTO PLAY.

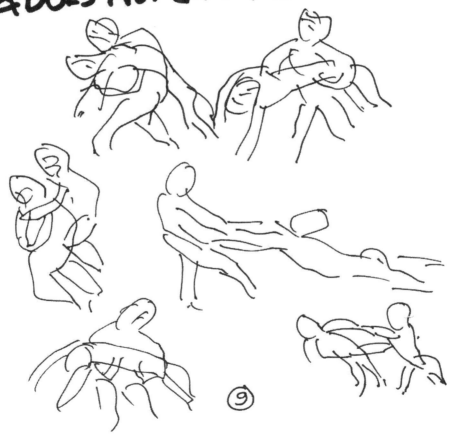

⑨

CONCERNING THE THIRD CATEGORY OF WAR FUNCTIONARIES, THE PRISONERS, THE CHAIRS BENEFIT ENORMOUSLY FROM BEING CHAIRS, SO THAT THEIR HUMANITY CANNOT GET IN THE WAY & THE PRISONERS CAN BE TREATED ACCORDING TO THE REQUIREMENTS OF WAR & BRUTALITY

BREAD&PUPPET
PRESS 2007

BREAD & PUPPET

KASPER 25

142

WHEN KASPER CUT HIS TOENAILS HE
CUT HIS TOE & HE ASKED:

145

THEY CUT NATURE + MAKE IT REAL ESTATE

THEY CUT THE TRUTH FROM THE FACTS &EMPLOY PHANTASY ART TO PROVE THE EXISTENCE OF WEAPONS OF MASS DESTRUCTION

⑥

THEY CUT ALL SENSE OUT OF THE
GOVERNMENT & MAKE IT HELPLESS
IN THE FACE OF THE

THEY CUT FROM THE OCCUPIERS SO THEY CAN APPLY TORTURE IN ABU GHRAIB ⑧

THEY CUT THE WRONG GOLS

OF INNOCENT PRISONERS IN GUANTANAMO (9)

BREAD&PUPPET
PRESS 2007
GLOVER   VT

BREAD & PUPPET

KASPER 26

THIS IS
KASPER'S
DIVINA
SHOPPING
COMEDIA

OR: HOW TO REDESIGN THE WORLD TO ACHIEVE
THE POLITICALLY CORRECT POST-MODERN PARADISE
— IN TWO PARTS —

156

158

NEXT YOU NEED

SCHOOLS TO TRAIN CITIZENS FOR THE PROPER WISHING & WANTING THAT RESULT IN THE PROPER QUANTITY OF SHOPPING

HAZEL

③

NEXT YOU NEED
A SECURITY SYSTEM

A SURVEILLANCE SYSTEM

A SPY SYSTEM ON DISSIDENTS

A LAW-ENFORCEMENT SYSTEM

TO ENSURE THE SAFETY OF PARADISE GOODS ⑤

NEXT YOU NEED THE **PARADISE CULINARY INSTITUTE**

WHERE CAR + LIMO-STEAKS, REFRIDGERATOR-FILLETS + CHOPPED-HIGHWAY-DESSERTS ARE OFFERED FOR POPULAR CONSUMPTION (ALL MEATS ARE SPICED WITH A SPRINKLE OF DISOBEDIENT CITIZEN-PEPPER) ⑥

162

NEXT YOU NEED THE TOTAL LIGHTBULB

WHICH ENLIGHTENS YOU ADEQUATELY TO ENJOY THE PRIVILEGES OF PARADISE-CITIZENSHIP (NOT ONLY YOUR OFFICE BUT YOUR BRAIN AS WELL) ⑦

THIS RESULTS IN THE TOTAL LIGHTBULB EXPORTS
WHICH REQUIRE THE DISSEMINATION OF THE
TOTAL LIGHTBULB RELIGION IN THE MOST DISTANT
REGIONS WHERE PEOPLE JUST LIVE BECAUSE
THEY DON'T KNOW ANY BETTER

THIS RESULTS IN THE TOTAL LIGHTBULB WARS
& THE FAMOUS VICTORY OVER ALL NON-BELIEVERS⑧

PART TWO: INFERNO

CONSISTING OF: FERTILITY DANCES OF UNTAMEABLE ELEMENTS LIKE WILD HORSES & TIGERS & WILD HORSE & TIGER-LIKE CITIZENS WHO CAN'T BE FITTED INTO THE PARADISE RE-EDUCATION PROGRAM

BREAD & PUPPET
PRESS 2007
GLOVER VERMONT

BREAD & PUPPET

KASPER 27

GENERAL KASPER'S
HEARTFELT DISPATCHES
TO HIS SOLDIERS.

172

174

175

10

180

BREAD & PUPPET
PRESS 2007
GLOVER VT

BREAD & PUPPET

KASPER 28

A JOB

NEXT:

LITTLE KASPER FINDS A JOB AS PRESIDENTIAL BELLY-SCRATCHER

OBVIOUSLY A PRESIDENT NEEDS TO FABRICATE PILES OF PATRIOTIC REVENGE & PHANTASTIC DESTRUCTION & THEREFORE NEEDS BELLY-SCRATCHING

REVENGE = MILITARY OPERATION = DEMO-CRATIZATION

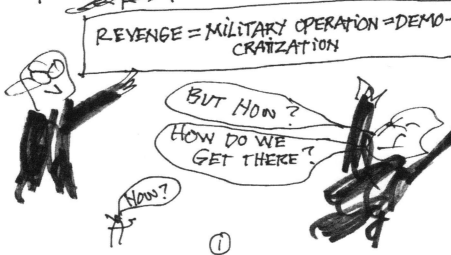

186

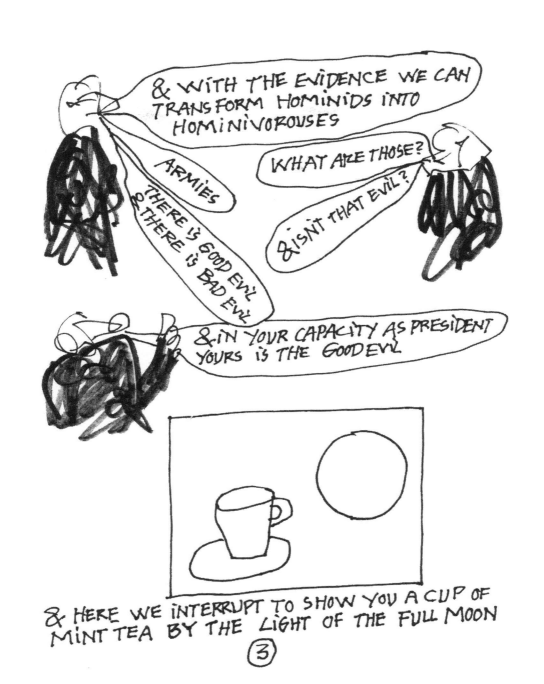

& HERE WE INTERRUPT TO SHOW YOU A CUP OF
MINT TEA BY THE LIGHT OF THE FULL MOON
③

188

AND THEN

AND HE FOUND A JOB AS A
CLEANER-UPPER OF THE MESS
THAT THE ABOVE-MENTIONED
INCIDENTS HAD CREATED

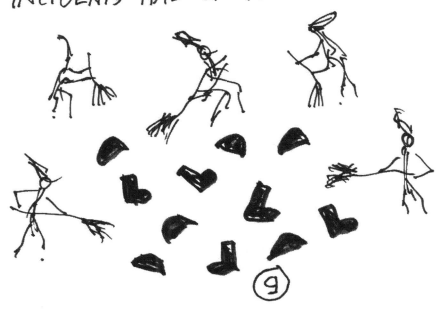

& THEREFORE WE SHOW YOU HERE
A PICTURE OF AN UPSIDE-DOWN TREE
IN SPRINGTIME

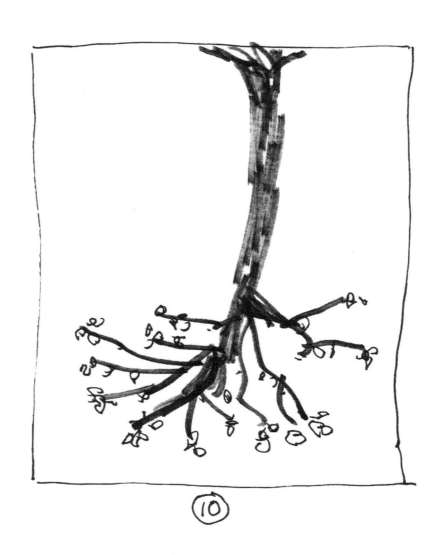

(10)

BREAD & PUPPET
PRESS   2007
GLOVER   VT

BREAD & PUPPET

KASPER 29

199

& DECORATED WITH ICE-PROOF DUCKS WHO SPENT ALL THEIR DAYS FROLICKING ON THE ICE. THE ONE-FOOT-IN-THE-GRAVE KASPER

5

WAS EXTREMELY WELL-HOUSED & WELL-FED IN THE COLONY & WAS EMPLOYED TO APPLY HIS ONE-FOOT-IN-THE-GRAVE EXPERTISE TO THE ITINERANT ART-PRODUCTS, AN ENDEAVOUR NOT TO BE TAKEN LIGHTLY.

6

BECAUSE ART IN ALL ITS FOOLISHNESS IS NEVERTHE-LESS THE ONLY CREDIBLE LINE OF FOODPRODUCTION FOR THE MOSTLY STARVING, THOUGH OVERFED, CITIZENS OF THE THIRD MILLENIUM THAT HAS ANY CHANCE TO SURVIVE THE PREDICTABLE SHORTAGES.

7

FOOD HAS ALWAYS OCCUPIED MANKIND'S TOP PRIORITY ATTENTION. COW, ELEPHANT & SONGBIRD ALIKE ARE TRADITIONALLY GROUNDUP FOR HAMBURGER MEAT.

8

9

1000 YEAR OLD TREES, PRAIRIES OF ETERNAL GRASS & THE MOST EXQUISITE FLOWER GARDENS OF MOTHER NATURE HAVE ALL BEEN SERVED AT OUR DINNER TABLES. AND

10

AS OUR TEETH & APPETITE IMPROVE & OUR STOMACH CAPACITY GAINS MOMENTUM, THE OCEANS & THE MOUNTAINS GET SWALLOWED UP & THE METALS FROM THE INNARDS OF THE EARTH —

11

WHETHER DISGUISED AS CARS OR SKYSCRAPERS — ARE ALL PART OF OUR DAILY DIET & ARE EXCRETED AS NON-COMPOSTABLE POOP, RECYCLED SOLELY BY THE BULLETMAKERS & PENTAGONS WHO ARE IN CHARGE OF POPULATION DECIMATION.

12

NATURALLY, THE CLUMSY ONE-FOOT-IN-THE-GRAVE KASPER CAN'T MOVE FAST ENOUGH, NOR DOES HIS LONG BEARD ALLOW HIM TO SPEAK ELOQUENTLY ENOUGH TO ADDRESS THE OBVIOUS NEEDS & REVIEW THE MANY PHANTASTIC PROPOSALS OF ARTISTIC FOOD PRODUCTION. DURING HIS SHORT STAY AT THE COLONY HE HAS BARELY HAD TIME TO APPRECIATE THE HORS D'OEUVRES — DELICATE SOUNDBITES MIXED WITH GARBAGE SALVAGE COMPOSITIONS — WELL SUITED FOR ANY MODERN ROYALTY'S PALATE. AND DINNER IS NOT EVEN READY YET!

FIRST, HUMAN HABITS HAVE TO BE ATTACKED! POST-MODERN STUCKNESS HAS TO BE CORRECTED! HUMAN DESIRE FOR MORE-THAN-MEETS-THE-EYE NEEDS TO BE SCHOOLED! THE SLUMPED-OVER, SEDENTARY HUMAN DANCE-BODY NEEDS TO BE STUNG BY BUMBLEBEES IN ORDER TO FIRE UP THE SECRET DANCES THAT LIE HIDDEN IN THE DISPASSIONATE SITTER'S FLESH! THE SEAT ITSELF MUST BE SUBJECTED TO DANCE LESSONS. AND INDEED THE EATING OF ART ITSELF IS AS YET AN INSUFFICIENT FORM OF EATING, CONFINED TO ELITIST CUSTOM + NOT GENERALLY UNDERSTOOD AS PLAIN EVERYDAY NOURISHMENT. WHERE DO WE START? BY RE-TRAINING FORKS & KNIVES? BY RE-DESIGNING DINNER FURNITURE? BY DIVING INTO THE ICY RIVER BEFORE WE EAT, IN IMITATION OF THE DIVINE DUCKS WHOM THE RIVERGOD MUST HAVE PUT THERE FOR THAT SPECIFIC PURPOSE? AFTER ALL, THE CONSEQUENCE OF ANY FOOD-INTAKE IS ALWAYS THE SAME: TO STRENGTHEN US SHORTLY BEFORE WE DIE.

(m)

203

A fomite is a medium capable of transmitting infectious organisms from one individual to another.

"The activity of art is based on the capacity of people to be infected by the feelings of others." Tolstoy, *What Is Art?*

Writing a review on Amazon, Good Reads, Shelfari, Library Thing or other social media sites for readers will help the progress of independent publishing. To submit a review, go to the book page on any of the sites and follow the links for reviews. Books from independent presses rely on reader to reader communications.

Visit http://www.fomitepress.com/FOMITE/Our_Books.html for more information or to order any of our books.

As It Is On Earth
Peter M Wheelwright

Dons of Time
Greg Guma

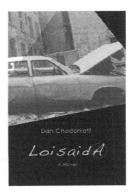

Loisaida
Dan Chodorkoff

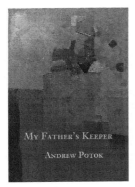

My Father's Keeper
Andrew Potok

My God, What Have We Done
Susan V Weiss

Rafi's World
Fred Russell

The Co-Conspirator's Tale
Ron Jacobs

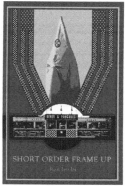

Short Order Frame Up
Ron Jacobs

All the Sinners Saints
Ron Jacobs

Travers' Inferno
L. E. Smith

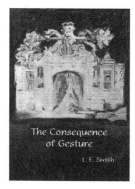

The Consequence of Gesture
L. E. Smith

Raven or Crow
Joshua Amses

Sinfonia Bulgarica
Zdravka Evtimova

The Good Muslim
of Jackson Heights
Jaysinh Birjépatil

The Moment Before an Injury
Joshua Amses

208

The Return of
Jason Green
Suzi Wizowaty

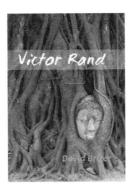

Victor Rand
David Brizeri

Zinsky the Obscure
Ilan Mochari

Body of Work
Andrei Guruianu

Carts and Other Stories
Zdravka Evtimova

Flight
Jay Boyer

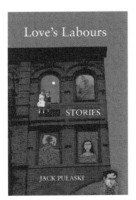

Love's Labours
Jack Pulaski

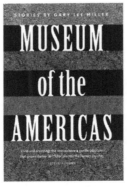

Museum of the Americas
Gary Lee Miller

Saturday Night at Magellan's
Charles Rafferty

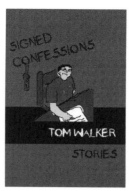

Signed Confessions
Tom Walker

Still Time
Michael Cocchiarale

Suite for Three Voices
Derek Furr

Unfinished Stories of Girls
Catherine Zobal Dent

Views Cost Extra
L. E. Smith

Visiting Hours
Jennifer Anne Moses

When You Remeber
Deir Yassin
R. L. Green

Alfabestiaro
Antonello Borra

Cycling in Plato's Cave
David Cavanagh

AlphaBetaBestiario
Antonello Borra

Entanglements
Tony Magistrale

Everyone Lives Here
Sharon Webster

Four-Way Stop
Sherry Olson

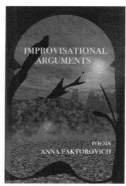

Improvisational
Arguments
Anna Faktorovitch

Loosestrife
Greg Delanty

Meanwell
Janice Miller Potter

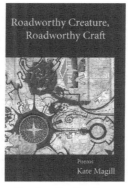

Roadworthy Creature
Roadworth Craft
Kate Magill

The Derivation of
Cowboys & Indians
Joseph D. Reich

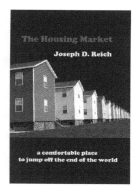

The Housing Market
Joseph D. Reich

The Empty Notebook
Interrogates Itself
Susan Thomas

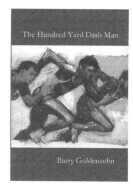

The Hundred Yard
Dash Man
Barry Goldensohn

The Listener Aspires
to the Condition of Music
Barry Goldensohn

The Way None
of This Happened
Mike Breiner

Screwed
Stephen Goldberg

Planet Kasper
Peter Schumann

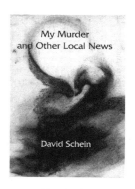

My Murder
and Other Local News
David Schein

Picking Up the Bodies
James F. Connolly

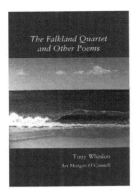

The Falkland Quartet
Tony Whedon

Companion Plants
Kathryn Roberts

Made in the USA
Monee, IL
24 October 2023

45159162R00122